Social Studies in First Grade

These are just a few of the things that your child will study in first grade:

- How to be a good citizen
- Patriotic symbols and traditions that honor the Commonwealth of Virginia and the United States
- Events in the history of our Commonwealth
- The contributions of influential Virginians
- The meaning of American holidays, such as Martin Luther King, Jr. Day; George Washington Day; and Independence Day
- How to use maps and globes
- Locating Virginia on maps and globes
- The difference between spending and saving money
- The importance of voting and how state and local government officials help communities
- Understanding that people make choices because they cannot have everything they want

Social Studies Standards of Learning

The first grade Social Studies curriculum is created by the Commonwealth of Virginia. Your child will be taking tests throughout the year to assess his or her understanding of the material and to become more comfortable with test-taking skills.

SOL Newsletters

As each new topic is introduced, you will receive an **SOL Newsletter**. Please notice which *Standard of Learning, Essential Knowledge*, and *Terms to Know* are being taught in class. These come directly from the Virginia Board of Education.

You will also find a section called **Learning at Home**. These are activities which you can do with your child to help reinforce the concepts being taught in class.

WE APPRECIATE YOUR HELP!

Learning at Home

Children learn new concepts best when they can associate them with things they already know. You can help build your child's background knowledge every day through conversation.

- Map skills are an important part of the social studies curriculum. Be on the lookout for a globe, a world map, a map of the United States, and a map of Virginia for your child to use at home. They will be useful throughout your child's school years. Maps of Virginia are often available at the Virginia Department of Transportation at no cost.

- Ask friends and relatives to send postcards from the different places they live or visit. Talk about these places and how they are different from or similar to our community.

- Visit the public library and get a library card. Check out books about Virginia to read together.

- Trips to museums and historical sites also help children develop an understanding of social studies. In first grade, students will learn about life in the past. Share with your child some of the things you used as a child. Ask grandparents to share stories of their childhoods. Help your child begin to understand the changes that take place over time. But most important of all, have fun seeing the world through your child's eyes.

IT'S GOING TO BE A GREAT YEAR!

CITIZENSHIP!

What rules do you follow in your home? Remind your child why we have rules.
· **To protect rights of people** · **To provide suggestions for good behavior**
· **To keep people safe**

Standards of Learning

1:10 *The student will apply the traits of a good citizen by:*
a) Focusing on fair play, exhibiting good sportsmanship, helping others, and treating others with respect; b) Recognizing the purpose of rules and practicing self-control; c) Working hard in school; d) Taking responsibility for one's own actions; e) Valuing honesty and truthfulness in oneself and others; f) Participating in classroom decision making through voting.

1:11 *The student will recognize the symbols and traditional practices that honor and foster patriotism in the United States by demonstrating respect for the American flag and learning about the Pledge of Allegiance.*

1:12 *The student will recognize the symbols and traditional practices that honor the Commonwealth of Virginia by:*
a) Identifying the Virginia flag, state capitol building, state bird, and state flower;
b) Describing why people have symbols and traditions.

ESSENTIAL KNOWLEDGE
Students can demonstrate good citizenship by:

- Playing fairly • Exhibiting good sportsmanship • Helping others
- Treating others with respect • Recognizing the purpose of rules
- Practicing self-control • Working hard in school
- Taking responsibility for one's own actions
- Valuing honesty and truthfulness in oneself and others
- Participating in classroom decision making

REASONS FOR VOTING: • To voice your opinion • To take part in the process

REASONS FOR RULES: • To protect the rights of people • To provide suggestions for good behavior • To keep people safe

TERMS TO KNOW:
- **American flag:** A patriotic symbol of the United States
- **Pledge of Allegiance:** A patriotic tradition that honors the people and the history of the United States. Citizens say the Pledge of Allegiance to demonstrate respect for the American flag and the United States.
- **symbol:** A picture or thing that stands for something else
- **tradition:** A custom or belief that is practiced or observed over a long period of time
- **patriotic:** Showing respect for and love of country and state

PATRIOTIC SYMBOLS OF THE COMMONWEALTH OF VIRGINIA
- Virginia flag • State capitol building located in Richmond
- Cardinal (the state bird) • Dogwood (the state flower)

People use patriotic symbols and traditions to honor the people and the history of Virginia. A tradition is a way of doing things that can be passed down from adults to children.

Learning at Home

Help reinforce the traits of good citizenship with a chart. Each time you see your child exhibiting a positive trait, offer praise and record the effort by drawing a star on the chart beside the trait. Work with your child to set a goal. When your child has earned the agreed upon number of stars, celebrate by sharing a favorite treat or spending a special afternoon together. Talk about how good it feels to do the right thing.

Election Day

When elections are held in your community, talk with your child about the process of voting. Who are the people involved? What types of jobs do they do in our community? Why is it important for good citizens to participate in the voting process? If possible, take your child with you.

Symbol-Searching

Help your child find various types of symbols in your community. How can you find the restroom in a local restaurant? What symbols are used? Often traffic signs are symbols. What do they mean? Symbols are used to show where hospitals are, to show reserved parking for people who have difficulty walking, and to help us find our favorite stores and restaurants. Help your child make a list of symbols and what they represent.

Together, find symbols of patriotism in your community. Challenge your child to count the number of American flags he or she sees on your way to the store. Where are they located? How are they used? If you have visited Washington, D.C., discuss the symbols of patriotism you saw there.

I AM A GOOD CITIZEN!

Name _____

Place a star beside each trait of good citizenship you see your child perform.

I played fairly.								
I showed good sportsmanship.								
I helped another person.								
I showed respect to other people.								
I understand why we need rules.								
I worked hard.								
I showed self-control.								
I took responsibility for my actions.								
I was truthful and honest at a difficult time.								
I used voting to help make a decision with my friends or family.								

PICTURE ANALYSIS

LOOK

Look carefully at the picture. Describe what you see.

What people and things do you see?
Where are they?
Are there any words in the picture?
What are they?
When you looked at the picture, what did you notice first? Why?

THINK

Think about the picture.

If there are people in the picture, what are they doing? Who do you think they are? Is this a picture from the past or the present? How can you tell? How was this picture made?
Is it a drawing, a painting, or a photograph?
What can you learn from this picture?

ASK

Ask questions about the picture.

What might happen next in the picture?
What questions do you have about the picture?
Remember, questions begin with "who," "what," "when," "where," "why," or "how."
Where could you find answers to your questions?

DO

Do show what you have learned.

Explain what you see in the picture to another student.
Tell one thing about the picture.
Write a sentence about the picture.
How does this picture help you understand the subject?

PATRIOTIC HEADBANDS
Which is your favorite symbol of Virginia? Cut it out and color it!

CARDINAL

VIRGINIA STATE FLAG

Dogwood

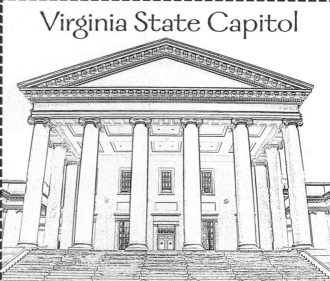

Virginia State Capitol

MATERIALS:

· Red, white, or blue Construction paper cut into 12" x 3" wide strips
· Crayons, scissors, and glue sticks
· Stapler

PROCEDURE:

1. Have students choose their favorite patriotic symbol from the above images. Ask them to cut it out and color it.

2. Have students glue their choice in the middle of the construction paper strip.

3. Staple the finished headbands and have the children wear them throughout the day.

A PATRIOT'S PUZZLER

Use the patriotic words listed below to complete the puzzle. Mark out each word after you use it.

Name _____

A L L E G I A N C E

FLAG
PATRIOTS
LIBERTY
EAGLE
RED
WHITE
BLUE
AMERICA
STARS
STRIPES
~~ALLEGIANCE~~

Challenge:
On the back of this paper write one sentence using at least six of these words.

9

Student Edition Do You Know?

1. **How can you show you are a good citizen?**

   _____

   _____

2. **Why do we have rules?**

   _____

   _____

3. **Why do people vote?**

   _____

   _____

4. **What are four patriotic symbols of Virginia?**

   _____

   _____

   _____

   _____

5. Name one patriotic symbol of the United States.

_____

- -

_____

6. Name a patriotic tradition that honors the people and history of the United States.

_____

- -

_____

7. Draw a picture of you being a good citizen in your classroom.

Write a sentence to explain how your actions help make the classroom a better place.

_____

- -

_____

_____

- -

_____

KEY WORDS: Chapter 1

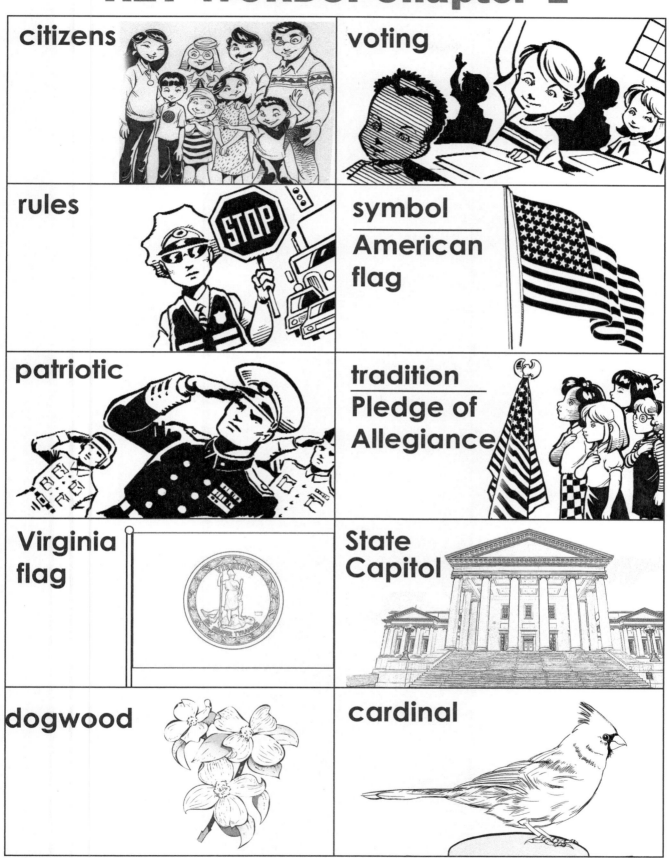

citizens	voting
rules	symbol American flag
patriotic	tradition Pledge of Allegiance
Virginia flag	State Capitol
dogwood	cardinal

VIRGINIA'S BIRD

Cut out and put your very own cardinal together.
Color the feathers red. Color the beak and feet yellow.
Write "Virginia" in the box.

CHAPTER 1 STUDY GUIDE

Good citizens show many positive traits.

 Good citizens play fairly.

Good citizens treat others with respect.

Good citizens show good sportsmanship.

 Good citizens help others.

Good citizens work hard in school.

Good citizens practice self-control.

Good citizens are honest and tell the truth.

Good citizens are responsible.

 Good citizens vote in classroom decisions.

Rules are made so everyone is treated fairly. Good citizens know rules are important.

WHAT DO RULES DO?

Rules protect the rights of people.

Rules keep people safe.

Rules show us how to behave.

Good citizens help make decisions in their classroom by voting.

Vote to voice your opinion! Vote to take part in the process!

Important words to know:

SYMBOL: *A picture or object that stands for something*

TRADITION: *A custom or belief that develops over a long period of time*

PATRIOTIC: *To feel respect for, or love of, your country and state*

Patriotic symbols and traditions honor the people and history of the United States and of Virginia.

The American flag is a patriotic symbol of the United States.

Citizens say the Pledge of Allegiance to demonstrate respect for the American flag and the United States.

These are patriotic symbols of the Commonwealth of Virginia:

Virginia's Capitol in Richmond

The state flag of Virginia

The cardinal— our state bird

The dogwood— our state flower

FIRST GRADE SOL NEWS

MAPS AND GLOBES

Exploring the world and learning to find our way around town!

Standards of Learning

1.5 *The student will develop map skills by:*
a) Recognizing basic map symbols, including references to land, water, cities, and roads
b) Using cardinal directions on maps
c) Identifying the shapes of the United States and Virginia on maps and globes
d) Locating Washington, D.C., the capital of the United States, and Richmond, the capital of Virginia, on a United States map
e) Constructing simple maps, including a title, map legend, and compass rose.

Terms to know

Map: A drawing that shows what places look like from above and where they are located
Globe: A round model of Earth
Symbol: A picture or thing that stands for something else
Cardinal directions: The directions of north, east, south, west
Title: The name of a map or what kind of map it is
Map legend: A list of shapes and symbols used on a map and an explanation of what each one stands for
Compass rose: A symbol that shows direction (north, east, south, and west) on a map

Map Symbols to Identify
Land • Water • Cities • Roads

The terms north, east, south, and west are used to determine location on simple maps.

Virginia and the United States may be located by their shapes on maps and globes.

The capital cities of Washington, D.C. and Richmond, Virginia, may be identified by using symbols on a United States map.

Learning at Home

• **Map skills are a big part of the Social Studies curriculum**. Be on the lookout for a globe, a world map, and a U.S. map for your child to use at home. Maps of Virginia are available at the Virginia Department of Transportation at no cost.

• **Practicing with maps and globes** is so important! Help your child make maps of your home and neighborhood.

• **Hide a treat** for your child in your home. Mark the location of the treat on a simple map of your home. Challenge your child to locate the treat using the map!

• **Make a map of your route to school**, the mall, or a friend's house. Have your child check off the landmarks as you travel.

• **When friends or family travel,** ask them to send postcards or bring back brochures. Have your child find these places on a map.

• **A visit to Washington, D.C.** or Richmond will make these capital cities more meaningful than just dots on a map. If possible, plan a family trip to one of these cities. Have fun learning together as a family!

Using Cardinal Directions on Maps:
RIDDLE TOWN

Directions: Use the cardinal directions and clues on the map to solve the riddle.

Riddle: What is green and blue and round all over?

Name _____

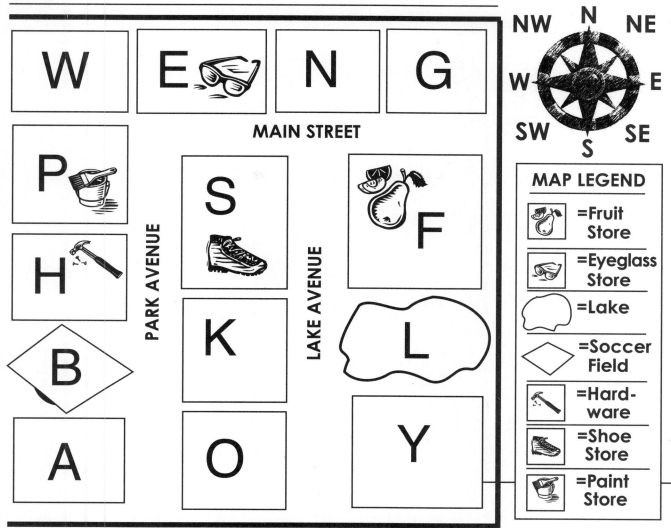

MAIN STREET

PARK AVENUE

LAKE AVENUE

MAP LEGEND

= Fruit Store

= Eyeglass Store

= Lake

= Soccer Field

= Hardware

= Shoe Store

= Paint Store

| This building is on the **SW** corner of Park Avenue. | This building is on the **NE** corner of Main Street. | This is a nice place to go fishing. | This place is very far south between Park and and Lake Avenues. | This is a great place to play soccer. | If you need help seeing better, this is a good store in which to shop. |

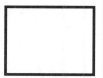

WHERE IN THE WORLD?

Name _____

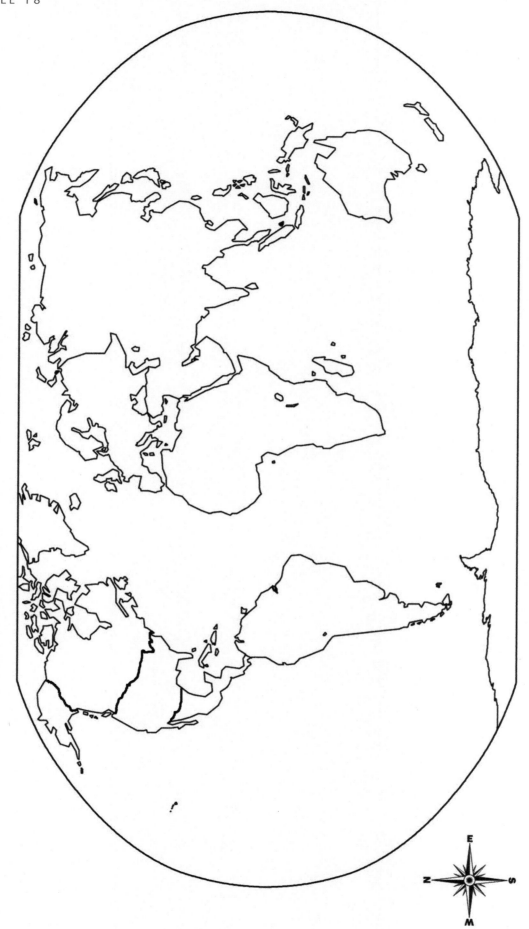

Find the United States of America. Color it red.
Color the rest of the land green. Color the ocean blue.

MAP PLACEMAT–U.S.A.

Use with the Virginia state map (Reproducible 20) to make a reversible placemat.

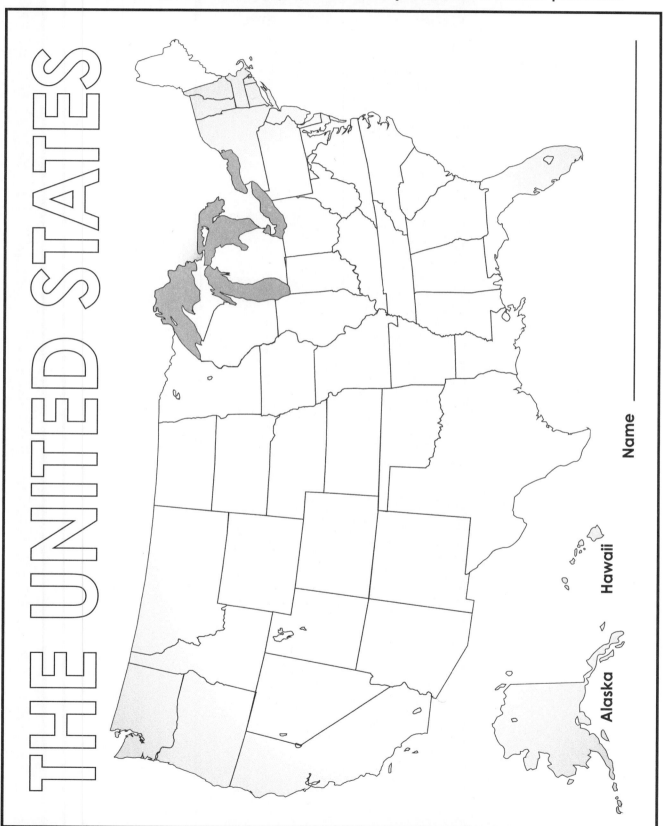

THE UNITED STATES

Name _____

Hawaii

Alaska

MAP PLACEMAT–VIRGINIA

Use with the continental U.S. map (Reproducible 19) to make a reversible snack placemat.

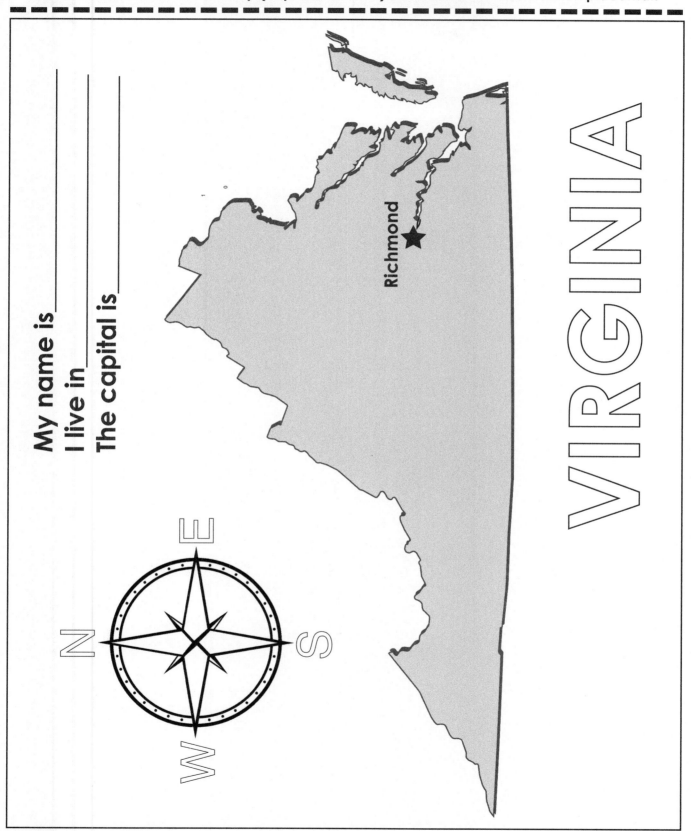

My name is _____

I live in _____

The capital is _____

Richmond

VIRGINIA

Student Edition Do You Know?

1. **What is the difference between a map and a globe?**

_____

- -

_____

_____

- -

_____

2. **List the four cardinal directions.**

_____

- -

_____

_____

- -

_____

Draw a compass rose that shows these directions.

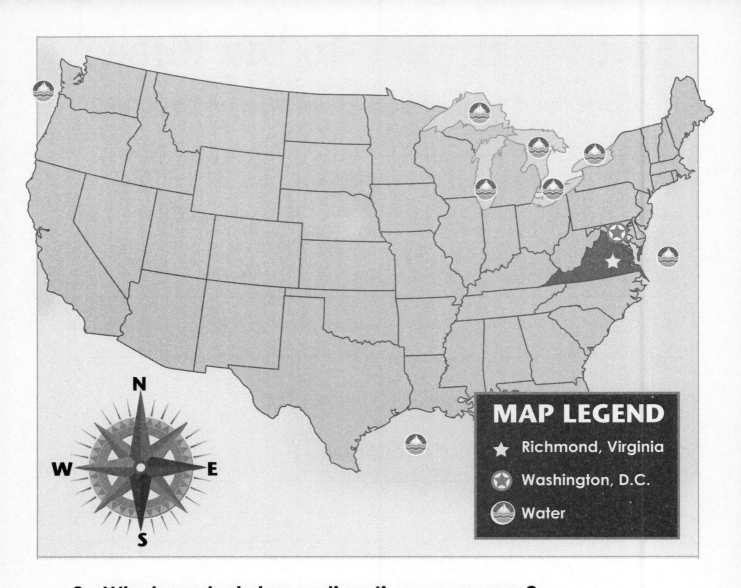

MAP LEGEND

★ Richmond, Virginia

✪ Washington, D.C.

🌊 Water

3. What symbol shows direction on a map?

_____

- -

_____

_____

4. Draw the symbol that represents Washington, D.C.

5. On the map above, what color is Virginia? _____

KEY WORDS: Chapter 2

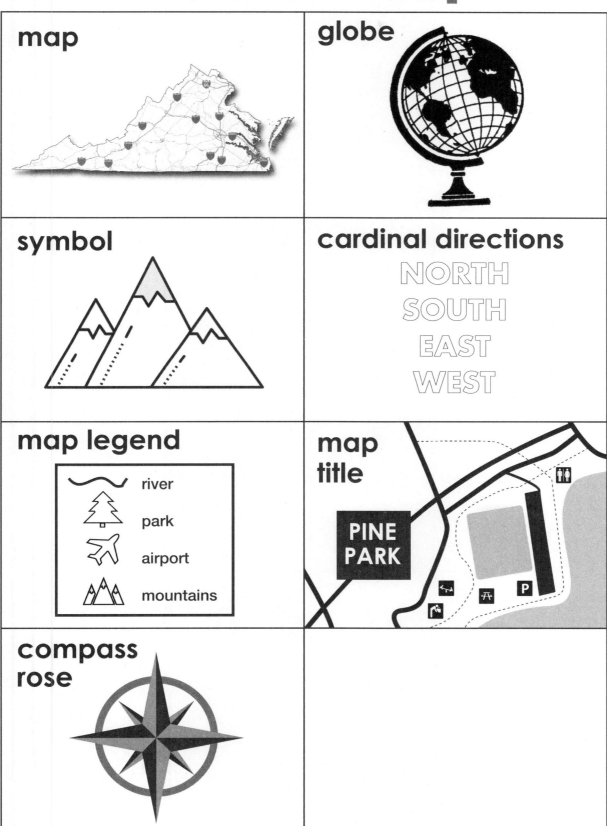

map	**globe**
symbol	**cardinal directions** NORTH SOUTH EAST WEST
map legend river park airport mountains	**map title** PINE PARK
compass rose	

CHAPTER 2 STUDY GUIDE

MAPS are drawings that show what places look like from above and where they are located.

GLOBES are round models of Earth.

PARTS OF A MAP

Town of Mountain Lakes

TITLE: Tells the name of a map or what kind of map it is.

MAP LEGEND

- - - roads

mountains

houses

offices

river

park

dock

trees

MAP LEGEND: A list of shapes and symbols used on a map with an explanation of what each one stands for.
A **symbol** is a picture or thing that stands for something else.

N
W E
S

COMPASS ROSE:

This symbol shows direction on a map.

The **cardinal directions** are north, east, south, and west.

A MAP OF VIRGINIA

This is the shape of Virginia. It looks like a triangle.
There are roads and cities listed on this map.

★ Richmond

● Roanoke

🛡 Highway

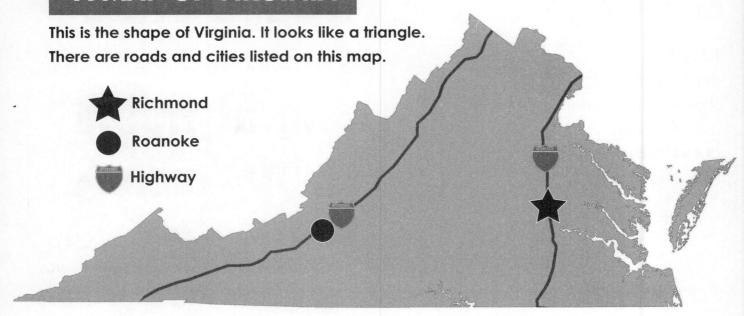

A MAP OF THE UNITED STATES

This is the shape of the United States. Richmond is the capital of Virginia.
Washington, D.C. is the capital of the United States.

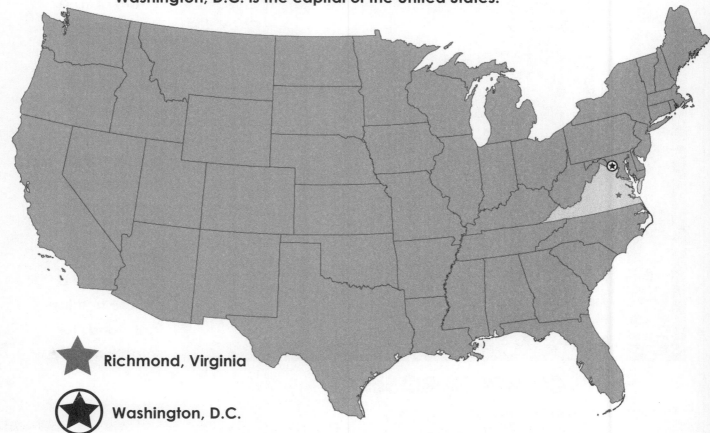

★ Richmond, Virginia

✪ Washington, D.C.

FIRST GRADE SOL NEWS

VIRGINIA LONG AGO

What was Virginia like 400 years ago?

Learning at Home

STANDARDS OF LEARNING

1.2 a *The student will demonstrate knowledge of Virginia history by describing important events and people in the history of the Commonwealth, including*
a) the settlement of Virginia at Jamestown

1.3 a, b, c
The student will describe the stories of influential people in the history of Virginia and their contributions to our Commonwealth, with emphasis on
a) Powhatan; b) Pocahontas;
c) Christopher Newport.

Virginia was settled by the English in the spring of 1607. When the first English settlers arrived, the Powhatan Indians had been living here for thousands of years. The new settlers and the Powhatan Indians had to find ways to live together on the same land.

Life was quite different in Virginia 400 years ago. The first settlers struggled to survive. They depended on the Powhatan Indians to help them learn how to build homes, hunt, fish, and grow crops. The landscape of Virginia was quite different 400 years ago as well.

To help your child with this unit, discuss the difference between the past and the present. Reminisce about times in the past that are relevant to your child (losing a tooth, having a birthday party, going on a family vacation, graduating kindergarten, etc.). Then discuss the state of Virginia and the place your family lives. Talk about how Virginia has a past as well. Together, predict what may have been different in Virginia 400 years ago.

If possible, take family trips to local historical places, such as:
- **Jamestown, Virginia**
- **Williamsburg, Virginia**
- **Yorktown, Virginia**

Essential Knowledge

Many different people and events helped shape Virginia's history. Virginia started at Jamestown over 400 years ago. Jamestown became the first permanent English settlement in North America.

Term to Know

Contribution: The act of giving or doing something

People to Know

Powhatan: He was an American Indian leader when the settlers came to Jamestown. He ruled over many tribes.

Pocahontas: She was an American Indian girl, daughter of Powhatan, who came with her father's people to visit the settlers at Jamestown. She worked to help the settlers receive food from the American Indians.

Christopher Newport: He was an English explorer who brought additional people and supplies to the Jamestown settlement.

PAST AND PRESENT

NAME

DIRECTIONS: Write things that happened in the past on the left under PAST.

Write things that happened in the present on the right under PRESENT.

If something happened in BOTH the past and the present, write it in the space in the middle.

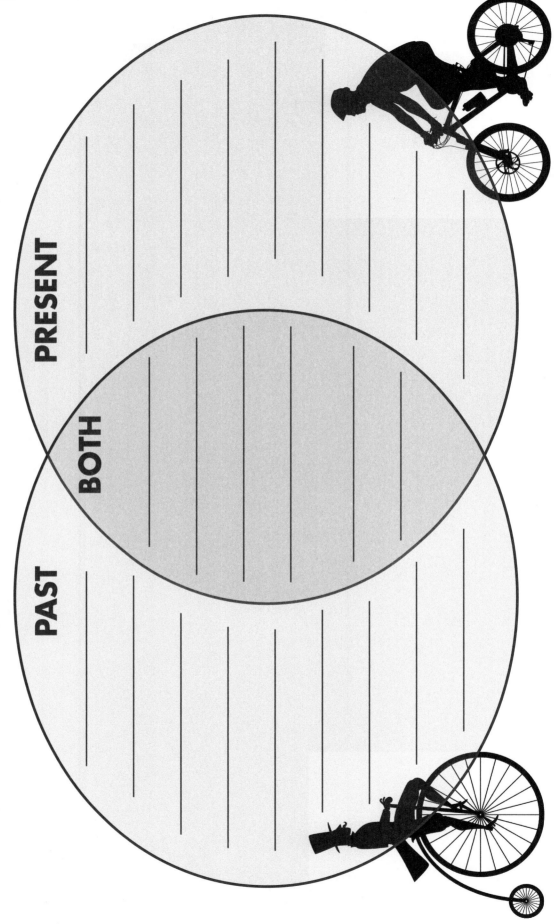

PRESENT

BOTH

PAST

Past and Present Sort

NAME _____

DIRECTIONS: Cut out the 8 boxes at the bottom.

Decide if the pictures are from the PAST or from the PRESENT.

Sort and glue the pictures into the correct place on the chart.

PAST	**PRESENT**

Virginia Then and Now

NAME _____

DIRECTIONS: Draw a picture of what you think the villages in Virginia looked like 400 years ago. Use page 37 of the textbook if you are not sure.

Virginia in the Past

DIRECTIONS: Draw a picture of what a Virginia town or city looks like in the present.

Virginia in the Present

A Virginia Indian Garden

NAME _____

DIRECTIONS: The Virginia Indians grew different crops. Read the picture graph. Answer the questions below the graph.

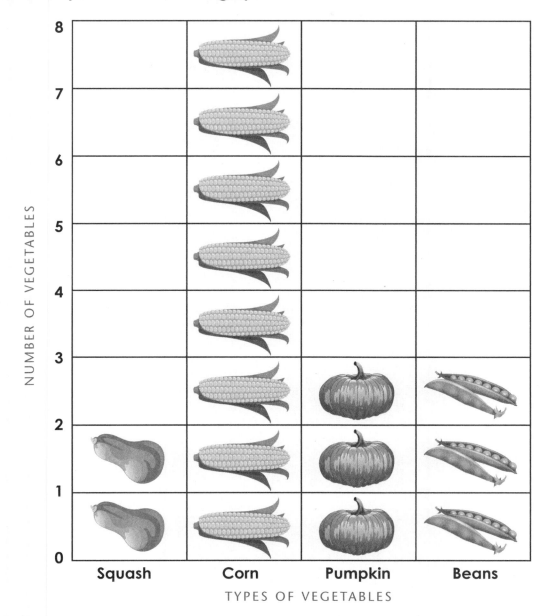

1. Which vegetable was grown the most? _____

2. Did the Virginia Indians grow more pumpkins or corn?_____

3. Did the Virginia Indians grow fewer squash or corn? _____

4. How many pumpkins did the Virginia Indians grow? _____

5. How many beans and pumpkins did they grow all together? _____

Powhatan Life

NAME _____

DIRECTIONS: The boxes at the bottom are activities of the Powhatan Indians 400 years ago.

Some of these boxes have pictures in them.

1. Draw a picture in each box at the bottom that does not have a picture.

2. Cut out the 8 boxes at the bottom. Sort the boxes as activities of Powhatan men, women, or children.

3. Glue the boxes in the correct column on the chart.

| POWHATAN MEN | POWHATAN WOMEN | POWHATAN CHILDREN |

| Cooking | Playing games | Farming | Fishing |
| Making clothes | Collecting firewood | Doing chores | Hunting |

Ask a Settler

NAME _____

DIRECTIONS: Write questions that you would ask a settler if you were able to go back in time.

QUESTION 1. _____

_____

_____

_____

QUESTION 2. _____

_____

_____

_____

QUESTION 3. _____

_____

_____

_____

From England to Virginia

NAME _____

Where did the settlers from England travel?

1.   The boats started in England. England is part of Europe.
     Trace the X on England with a green crayon.

2.   The boats traveled across the Atlantic Ocean.
     Color the Atlantic Ocean blue.

3.   The boats stopped in Virginia. Virginia is part of North America.
     Trace the X on Virginia with a black crayon.

4.   Trace the line from England to Virginia with a red crayon.

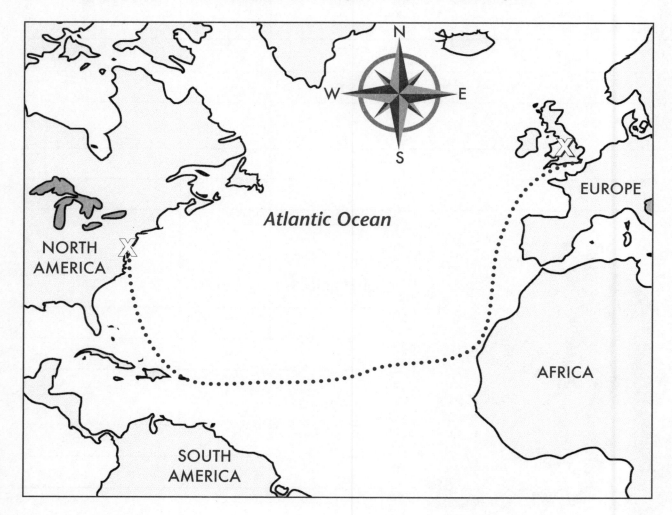

Wanted...But...So...

NAME _____

DIRECTIONS: Think about the English coming to Virginia. What did the English want? What was stopping the newcomers from getting what they wanted? What did the English have to do when they met the Powhatan Indians? Write about it here!

The English settlers wanted...

_____

_____

_____

But..._____

_____

_____

_____

So..._____

_____

_____

_____

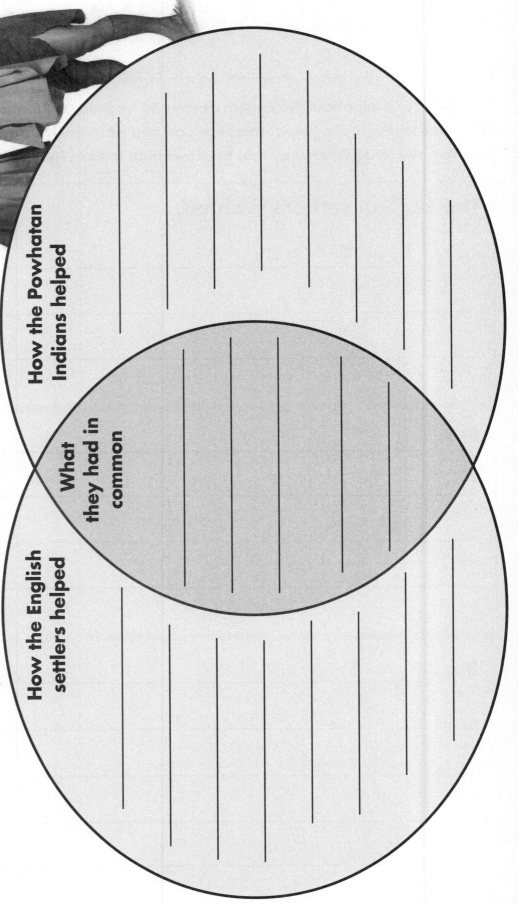

HOW THEY HELPED

NAME _____

DIRECTIONS: Fill in the Venn diagram. On the left side, list ways the English settlers helped the Powhatan Indians. On the right side, list ways the Powhatan Indians helped the English settlers. In the middle, write anything they had in common.

How the Powhatan Indians helped

What they had in common

How the English settlers helped

Do You Agree?

DIRECTIONS:

Read each statement below.
Decide if you AGREE or DISAGREE
with each one.

Your teacher will tell you where to write
your answer.

BEFORE Reading		Statements	AFTER Reading	
Agree	Disagree		Agree	Disagree
		1. Powhatan was a strong American Indian leader.		
		2. Powhatan ruled over one small tribe in Virginia.		
		3. Pocahontas was Powhatan's wife.		
		4. Pocahontas visited the settlers at Jamestown when she was a girl.		
		5. Pocahontas helped the settlers get food.		

Powhatan Was...

DIRECTIONS: Write adjectives that describe Powhatan.

Pocahontas Was...

DIRECTIONS: Write adjectives that describe Pocahontas.

Contribution Word Map

NAME _____

DIRECTIONS: Write the word "contribution" in the center of this organizer.

- Write the definition of "contribution" in the first box. Then draw a picture to help you remember the definition.

- Draw or write an example of a contribution. Draw or write the opposite of a contribution.

Write a definition.	**Draw a picture.**
Write or draw an example.	**Write or draw the opposite.**

Student Edition Do You Know?

1. Where did Virginia start over 400 years ago?

_____

_____

2. Who was the American Indian leader who ruled over many tribes when the settlers arrived in Virginia?

_____

_____

3. Who was Pocahontas?

_____

_____

_____

_____

4. How did Pocahontas help the settlers?

_____

- -

_____

_____

- -

_____

5. What contribution did Christopher Newport make to the Jamestown settlement?

_____

- -

_____

_____

- -

_____

Key Words: Chapter 3

explorer

Jamestown

Powhatan

Pocahontas

Christopher Newport

contribution

First Americans Word Search

Name _____

We use many American Indian words, such as PARKA and HAMMOCK, when we speak. Some of them are hidden in this puzzle. Circle each word when you find it and then cross it off the list. Can you find all of them?

Find:
~~RACCOON~~
PUMPKIN
SKUNK

CHIPMUNK
MOOSE
SQUASH
CANOE

COCOA
POTATO
SHARK
TOMATO

C	G	R	R	R	C	O	C	O	C	O	A	M
H	C	A	A	F	P	F	F	F	F	C
I	A	C	C	T	O	M	A	T	O
F	N	C	C	F	T	F	S	S	S
M	O	O	S	E	A	F	K	H	Q
F	E	O	O	F	T	B	U	A	U
F	F	N	N	F	O	F	N	R	A
C	H	I	P	M	U	N	K	K	S
P	U	M	P	K	I	N	F	F	H

CHAPTER 3 STUDY GUIDE

Virginia started at Jamestown over 400 years ago.
Jamestown became the first permanent English settlement in North America.

POWHATAN
He was an American Indian leader when the settlers came to Jamestown. He ruled over many tribes.

POCAHONTAS
She was Powhatan's daughter. She came with her father's people to visit the Jamestown settlers. She worked to help the settlers receive food from the American Indians.

PEOPLE AND TERMS TO KNOW

CHRISTOPHER NEWPORT

He was an English explorer who brought more people and supplies to the Jamestown settlement.

CONTRIBUTION

The act of giving or doing something

FIRST GRADE
SOL
NEWS

VIRGINIA IN THE 1700s

What was Virginia like after Jamestown?

STANDARDS OF LEARNING

1.2a *The student will demonstrate knowledge of Virginia history by describing important events and people in the history of the Commonwealth, including* b) famous Virginians, such as George Washington and Thomas Jefferson, who helped form a new nation

People to Know

George Washington: He was born in Virginia. He was a leader who helped develop the country. He was the first president of the United States. He is known as the "Father of Our Country." He led the fight for freedom from England and helped establish a new country.

Thomas Jefferson: He was born in Virginia. He was the third president of the United States. He was a leader who helped develop a new country.

Learning at Home

150 years after the settlement of Jamestown, Virginia saw many changes. The colony of Virginia expanded and new cities were built. The Powhatan Indians, who were instrumental in the foundation of Jamestown, were displaced. Fewer and fewer Powhatan Indians lived in the area as the colony grew.

There were hard times for other groups during this colonial time period as well. The practice of slavery expanded throughout the colony. The king of Great Britain began heavily taxing the American colonies. The colonists felt the taxes were unfair. They became frustrated under the control of Great Britain. Eventually, a war broke out between the colonies and Great Britain.

From the turmoil of the American Revolution, a hero emerged. George Washington was the leader of the army who led the fight for freedom from England. George Washington was our nation's first president and is known as the "Father of Our Country." Another strong leader who helped form our new nation was Thomas Jefferson. He was our third president and was also born in Virginia. Thomas Jefferson authored the Declaration of Independence that declared the freedom of the colonies from Great Britain.

There are many informative children's picture books available online or from your local library. Check out an age appropriate biography about one of these famous Virginians to learn more. There are also local places to visit with your child that will support the learning. Consider a family trip to:

- **Colonial Williamsburg**
- **Mount Vernon**
  The home of George Washington
- **Washington, D.C.**
  The home of the Washington Monument
- **University of Virginia**
  The college Thomas Jefferson founded
- **Monticello**
  The home of Thomas Jefferson

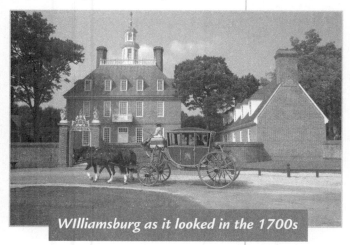
WIlliamsburg as it looked in the 1700s

Virginia Leaders KWL

DIRECTIONS:

List what *you already know* about Virginia and its great past leaders under the **K**.

List what you *want to know* about Virginia's past leaders under the **W**.

When you finish reading the chapter, list what you learned under the **L**.

<u>K</u>now	<u>W</u>ant to know	<u>L</u>earned
_____	_____	_____
_____	_____	_____
_____	_____	_____
_____	_____	_____
_____	_____	_____
_____	_____	_____
_____	_____	_____
_____	_____	_____
_____	_____	_____
_____	_____	_____

Hard Times NAME _____

DIRECTIONS: In the top box, write and draw about a hard time you have had
(For example: a fight with a sibling, or a lost pet, or a fall from a bike…).
In the bottom box, write and draw about how you got through that hard time.

MY HARD TIME

I had a hard time when _____

_____

_____

HOW I GOT THROUGH MY HARD TIME

I got through my hard time by_____

_____

_____

Our Class Declaration

NAME _____

DIRECTIONS: Write good citizenship rules for the class to follow.

Declaration of Good Citizenship

Ask George Washington

NAME _____

DIRECTIONS: Write a list of questions that you would like to ask George Washington.

Question 1

_____

- -

_____

Question 2

_____

- -

_____

Question 3

_____

- -

_____

Question 4

_____

- -

_____

Question 5

_____

- -

_____

Read All About It

DIRECTIONS: Design and write a newspaper article about George Washington and his contributions to Virginia. Don't forget to add a heading to your article!

The Virginia Tribune

The Commonwealth's Most Trusted News Source

Written by _____

George Washington's Life

NAME _____

DIRECTIONS: Complete the chart with facts about George Washington.

George Washington was born in ___?__.	_____ - _____
George Washington was our ___?___ president.	_____ - _____
George Washington's nickname was ___?__.	_____ - _____
One of George Washington's contributions was ___?__.	_____ - _____ _____ - _____

The President Song

Sing to the tune of "Wheels on the Bus."

The U.S.A. has leaders who
Leaders who
Leaders who
The U.S.A. has leaders who
We call presidents.

The first president was Washington
Washington
Washington
The first president was Washington
He was number one.

The third president was Jefferson
Jefferson
Jefferson
The third president was Jefferson
He was number three.

Thomas Jefferson's Life

NAME _____

DIRECTIONS: Complete the chart with facts about Thomas Jefferson.

Thomas Jefferson was born in ___?___.	
Thomas Jefferson was our ___?___ president.	
Thomas Jefferson's contributions were ___?___.	

Student Edition Do You Know?

1. **Who was the first president of the United States?**

   _____

   -

   _____

2. **Who was the third president of the United States?**

   _____

   -

   _____

3. **Where were Presidents Washington and Jefferson born?**

   _____

   -

   _____

4. **Who is called the "Father of Our Country"?**

   _____

   -

   _____

5. **If you could ask George Washington one question, what would it be?**

_____

- -

_____

_____

- -

_____

6. **If you could ask Thomas Jefferson one question, what would it be?**

_____

- -

_____

_____

- -

_____

CHAPTER 4 STUDY GUIDE

These famous Virginians helped form our new nation.

IMPORTANT PERSON	GEORGE WASHINGTON	THOMAS JEFFERSON
BIRTHPLACE	Virginia	Virginia
PRESIDENT	<u>First</u> president of the United States	<u>Third</u> president of the United States
CONTRIBUTION	1. He was a leader who helped develop the country. 2. He is known as the "Father of Our Country." 3. He led the fight for freedom from England. 4. He helped establish a new country.	1. He was a leader who helped develop the country.

FIRST GRADE SOL NEWS

THE NEXT 200 YEARS IN VIRGINIA

Through difficult times, new heroes emerge!

STANDARDS OF LEARNING

1.3 *The student will describe the stories of influential people in the history of Virginia and their contributions to our Commonwealth, with emphasis on*
d) Maggie L. Walker
e) Arthur R. Ashe, Jr.

People to Know

Maggie L. Walker:
She was the first African American woman in the United States to establish a bank and become a bank president.

Arthur R. Ashe, Jr.:
He was the first African American winner of a major men's tennis singles championship. He was a leader for civil rights and worked for equality for all people.

Learning at Home

Arthur R. Ashe, Jr.

Maggie L. Walker

Both Maggie Walker and Arthur Ashe became civil rights leaders who worked for equality for everyone. In first grade, we use the lives of these two amazing people as examples for behavior in the classroom. We analyze the choices these historical figures made to use as a model for how to treat each other.

At home, have discussions with your child about "fairness" and "equality." Discuss how to share. Role play problem-solving strategies together. Teach your child how to come to a resolution, even if there are issues or differences of opinion between partners or groups.

A good way to practice this at home is through old-fashioned board games. Play a game of Monopoly as a family. Play checkers, cards, or dominoes. These games offer a chance to discuss taking turns and having patience. The games give children the opportunity to win graciously and lose gracefully.

My Contributions

NAME _____

DIRECTIONS: Write and draw about how you contribute to your classroom.
Write and draw about how you contribute to your home.

I contribute in my classroom when I …

I contribute at home when I …

Contribution Sort

NAME —————————————————————————

DIRECTIONS: Cut apart the pictures at the bottom of the page. Sort the pictures in the chart. Glue the pictures in the correct category.

Contribution	Not a Contribution

Maggie Walker's Pennies

NAME _____

DIRECTIONS: Cut apart the Maggie L. Walker facts at the bottom of the page. Use pages 72 and 73 to fill in each blank. Glue the Maggie L. Walker facts onto the piggy bank.

Maggie L. _____ was an African American woman

Maggie L. Walker was born in _____

Maggie L. Walker started a _____

Maggie L. Walker became a bank _____

83

Maggie Walker's Home

NAME

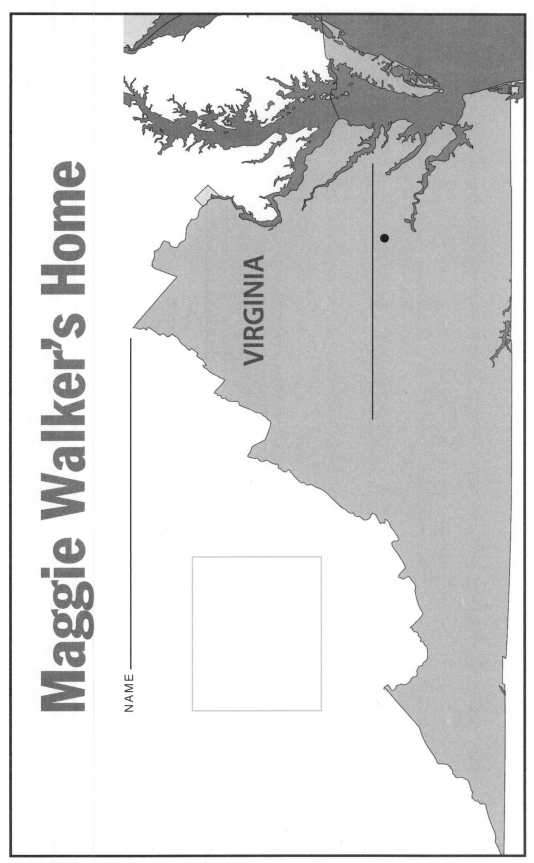

VIRGINIA

DIRECTIONS: Label Richmond, Virginia. Cut out the picture of Maggie L. Walker. Glue the picture of Maggie L. Walker in the box beside the map.

Arthur Ashe's Racket

NAME —————————————————————

DIRECTIONS: Create your own tennis racket with pictures, patterns, coloring, and words.

Know It!

NAME _____

DIRECTIONS: Work as a group to complete the graphic organizer.

Define it!	**Write a sentence using the word!**
_____	_____
_____	_____
_____	_____
_____	_____
Draw it!	**Write the word 2 times!**
	_____
	_____
	_____

Walker and Ashe

NAME _____

DIRECTIONS: Cut, sort, and glue the phrases into the correct category.

Maggie L. Walker	Arthur R. Ashe, 

✂ -

African American woman	Won a major tennis tournament
African American man	Was from Richmond, Virginia
Started a bank	Was from Richmond, Virginia
Played tennis	Worked for civil rights
Was a bank president	Worked for civil rights

Student Edition Do You Know?

1. Who was the first African American woman in the United States to open a bank and become its president?

   _____

   _____

2. Who was the first African American winner of a major men's tennis championship?

   _____

   _____

3. Arthur R. Ashe, Jr. was a leader for civil rights, and he worked for equality for all people. What do you think "equality" means?

   _____

   _____

   _____

   _____

4. **If you could ask Maggie L. Walker one question, what would it be?**

_____

- -

_____

_____

- -

_____

5. **If you could ask Arthur R. Ashe, Jr. one question, what would it be?**

_____

- -

_____

_____

- -

_____

CHAPTER 5 STUDY GUIDE

A contribution is the act of giving or doing something.

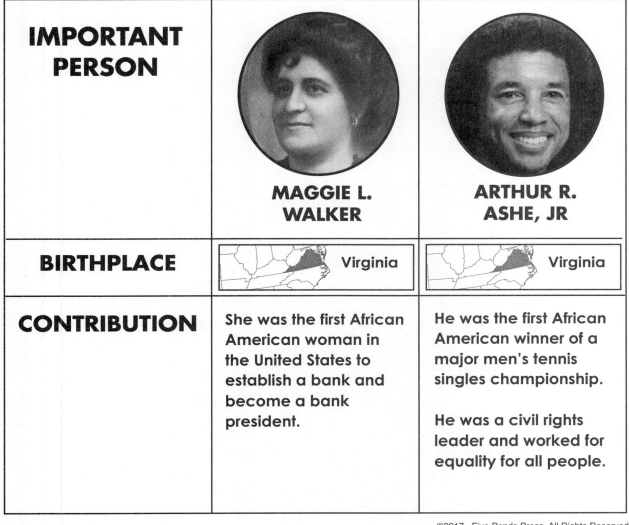

IMPORTANT PERSON	MAGGIE L. WALKER	ARTHUR R. ASHE, JR
BIRTHPLACE	Virginia	Virginia
CONTRIBUTION	She was the first African American woman in the United States to establish a bank and become a bank president.	He was the first African American winner of a major men's tennis singles championship. He was a civil rights leader and worked for equality for all people.

FIRST GRADE SOL NEWS

LET'S CELEBRATE

Time to learn more about the people and events that shaped our nation!

Standards of Learning

1.4 *The student will describe the lives of people associated with major holidays, including:*
a) George Washington Day (Presidents' Day); b) Independence Day (Fourth of July); and c) Martin Luther King, Jr. Day.

Learning at Home
Special Days!

As Americans, we honor and remember people and events that have shaped our lives. In this unit your child will learn about three important holidays that are celebrated to remember important leaders and events of the past:

- **Martin Luther King, Jr. Day**
- **George Washington Day (Presidents' Day)**
- **Independence Day (Fourth of July)**

To support this learning at home, study these important facts about the holidays listed below:

• **Holiday:** A day on which something or someone is honored or remembered

• **George Washington Day (Presidents' Day):** This is a day to remember all United States presidents, especially George Washington. It is observed in February.

• **Independence Day (Fourth of July):** This is a day to remember when America became a new country. It is sometimes called America's birthday. It is observed in July.

• **Martin Luther King, Jr. Day:** This is a day to remember an African American leader who worked so that all people would be treated fairly. It is observed in January.

Ways to help your child during this unit include:

- Discuss the concepts of fairness and equality.
- Talk about the importance of perseverance and courage.
- Discuss the necessity for education and working hard at school.
- Brainstorm ideas for helping others and how to share.
- Role play common student problems and how to solve them (For example, a conflict with a friend or sibling, or how to deal with a bully situation at school).

Special U.S. Holidays

NAME _____

DIRECTIONS: Circle the symbols that represent an American holiday.
Remember—a symbol is something that stands for something else.

A Holiday Song

NAME _____

DIRECTIONS: Sing this to the tune of "Twinkle, Twinkle Little Star."

Holidays are special days

We celebrate in many ways

We honor and remember too

Those who helped both me and you

Holidays are special days

We celebrate in many ways

How Many Holidays?

NAME _____

DIRECTIONS: Write the names of as many holidays as you know.

_____

_ _

_____

_____

_ _

_____

_____

_ _

_____

_____

_ _

_____

I can think of this many holidays: _____

Favorite Holidays

NAME _____

DIRECTIONS: Use data to make a graph about the holidays your class celebrates.

NUMBER OF STUDENTS

20
19
18
17
16
15
14
13
12
11
10
9
8
7
6
5
4
3
2
1
0

NAME OF HOLIDAY

1. Which holiday is celebrated the most?_____

2. Which holiday is celebrated the least?_____

3. Are there any holidays that have an equal number?_____

4. Which holiday is your favorite?_____

Honoring Dr. King

NAME _____

DIRECTIONS: Read the descriptions at the bottom. Cut out the FIVE descriptions that are TRUE about Martin Luther King, Jr. Glue them onto the web.

✂ -

He gave speeches and led marches.	A holiday in his honor is observed in January.	He was a leader.	He was an American Indian.
A holiday in his honor is observed in July.	He was a bank president.	He was an African American.	He worked hard so all were treated fairly.

I Have a Dream

NAME _____

DIRECTIONS: Martin Luther King, Jr. had a dream that all people would be treated fairly. Draw a picture of your dream for our classroom. Then write about it. What can we do so that all people are treated fairly at school?

This is my Dream ...

In our classroom, I have a dream that...

_____

_____

_____

_____

_____

_____

A HOLIDAY VENN

NAME _____

DIRECTIONS: Cut out the 8 boxes at the bottom. Read and sort them onto the Venn diagram. Check your answers and then glue them down.

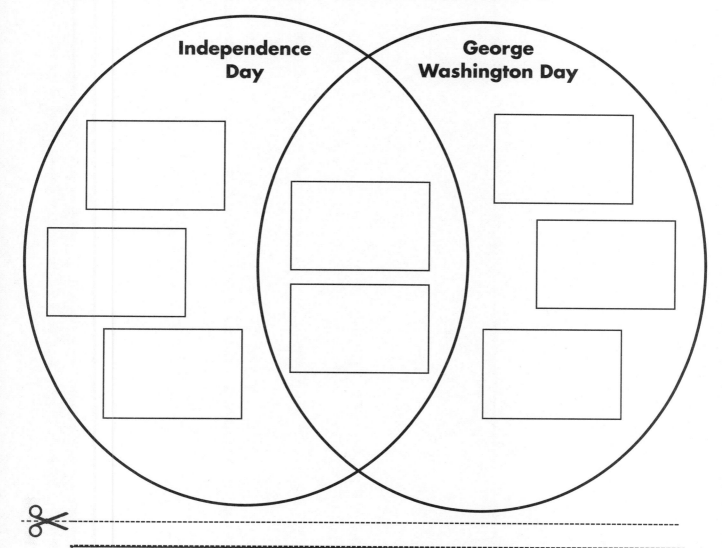

It is a holiday.	It is observed in July.	It honors George Washington.	It is America's birthday.
It is observed in February.	It honors all presidents.	It reminds us of the day America became a new country.	It is important to the citizens of the U.S.A.

CREATE A HOLIDAY

NAME _____

A drawing of my special person:

If I were to create a holiday, it would honor and

remember _____.

The holiday would be called _____

_____.

On this holiday, we would celebrate by

_____.

America's Special Days

NAME _____

DIRECTIONS: Cut out and read the boxes at the bottom. Sort and glue the boxes in the correct places on the chart.

Martin Luther King, Jr. Day	George Washington Day	Independence Day

- -

Observed in July	Remembers a man who worked so all people would be treated fairly	Can be called Fourth of July or America's birthday
Honors America's first president and all other presidents	Observed in January	Honors an African American leader
Honors when America became a country	Can be called Presidents' Day	Observed in February

Student Edition Do You Know?

1. **Why do we celebrate holidays?**

   _____

   -

   _____

   _____

   -

   _____

2. **Why do we honor Martin Luther King, Jr.?**

   _____

   -

   _____

   _____

   -

   _____

3. **What is the name of the holiday when Americans remember all the United States presidents?**

   _____

   -

   _____

4. Why is Independence Day also called America's birthday?

_____

- -

_____

_____

- -

_____

_____

- -

_____

CHAPTER 6 STUDY GUIDE

A <u>holiday</u> is a day on which something or someone is honored or remembered.

MARTIN LUTHER KING, JR. DAY

This is a day to remember an African American leader who worked so that all people would be treated fairly.

JANUARY

SUN	MON	TUE	WED	THU	FRI	SAT
				1	2	3
4	5	6	7	8	9	10
11	12	13	14	15	16	17
18	19	20	21	22	23	24
25	26	27	28	29	30	31

GEORGE WASHINGTON DAY (also known as Presidents' Day)

This is a day to remember all United States presidents, especially George Washington.

FEBRUARY

SUN	MON	TUE	WED	THU	FRI	SAT
	1	2	3	4	5	6
7	8	9	10	11	12	13
14	15	16	17	18	19	20
21	22	23	24	25	26	27
28	29					

INDEPENDENCE DAY (also known as Fourth of July)

This is a day to remember when America became a new country. It is sometimes called America's birthday.

JULY

SUN	MON	TUE	WED	THU	FRI	SAT
						1
2	3	4	5	6	7	8
9	10	11	12	13	14	15
16	17	18	19	20	21	22
23 30	24 31	25	26	27	28	29

FIRST GRADE SOL NEWS

LIVING IN VIRGINIA

Standards of Learning

1.2 *The student will demonstrate knowledge of Virginia history by describing important events and people in the history of the Commonwealth, including*
c) life in Virginia today, including food, clothing, shelter, transportation, and recreation.

1.6 *The student will develop a geographic understanding that*
b) the landforms of Virginia affect the places people live.

Essential Knowledge

The location, climate, and physical surroundings of Virginia affect the way people meet their basic wants today. This includes the
- foods they eat
- clothing they wear
- types of houses they build.

Communities in Virginia use various types of transportation to meet their needs.

The geography of Virginia affects how people travel from one place to another and determines what is available for recreation.

Terms to Know

climate: The kinds of weather an area has over a long period of time

physical surroundings: Land and bodies of water present in a given location

season: Any one of the four phases of the year (spring, summer, fall, or winter)

location: The place where a particular point or object exists on the surface of Earth

landform: A shape or feature of Earth's surface

The climate of Virginia is mild.
Virginia has four distinct seasons that include spring, summer, fall, and winter.
Landforms affect where people build houses and communities.
Location, climate, and physical surroundings affect the way people in Virginia meet their basic wants.

Learning at Home

Take note of the physical surroundings and landforms in your community as you explore the outdoors with your child. Weather permitting, take "geography walks" through your neighborhood together. Be on the lookout for hills, valleys, mountains, streams, and other bodies of water.

Show your child a variety of thermometers, and record daily temperatures throughout a season.

Discuss weather patterns and how those patterns determine what people wear each day. Have your child help pick out his/her own clothes based on those weather patterns.

Involve your child when you travel. Share maps of where you are going and use GPS devices together.

As you go out shopping or exploring the neighborhood, point out various types of transportation used by members of your community.

LANDFORMS
CAUSE AND EFFECT

Name _____

DIRECTIONS: Look at each picture in the CAUSE column. Draw or write an EFFECT that would happen as a result of each cause.

CAUSE

EFFECT

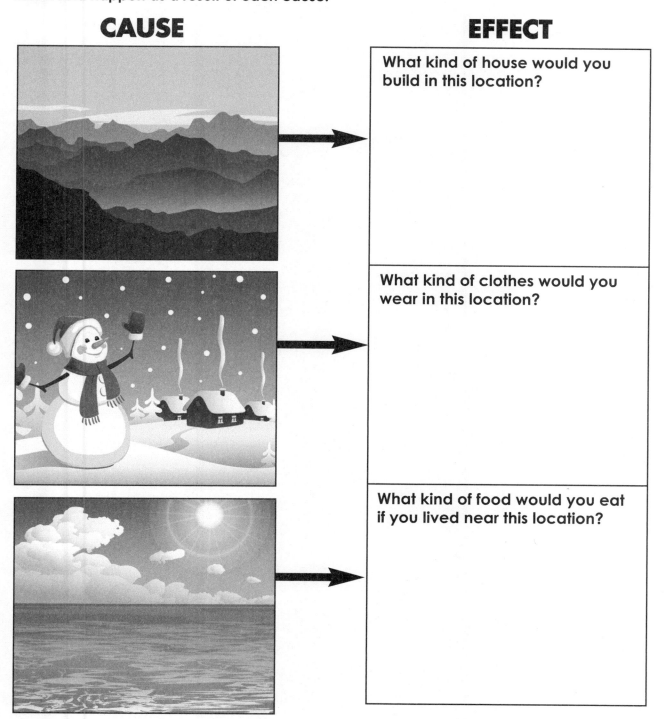

What kind of house would you build in this location?

What kind of clothes would you wear in this location?

What kind of food would you eat if you lived near this location?

LANDFORMS SORT

Name _____

DIRECTIONS: Cut out the eight boxes below. Sort the pictures under the correct landform names.

Hills	Valleys	Mountains	Coastal Plains

The Geography Song

**Sung to the tune of
"If You're Happy and You Know It."**

The climate is the weather over time.
The climate is the weather over time.
The climate is the weather
In Virginia it is mild.
Oh, the climate is the weather over time.

Surroundings are the water and the land.
Surroundings are the water and the land.
They are in a location
And affect the way we live.
Oh, surroundings are the water and the land.

The seasons are the phases of the year.
The seasons are the phases of the year.
Seasons of Virginia are spring,
summer, fall, and winter
Oh, the seasons are the phases of the year.

A location is a place on planet Earth.
A location is a place on planet Earth.
The location of Virginia
is on the southeast coast.
Oh, a location is a place on planet Earth.

A landform is the shape of Earth's surface.
A landform is the shape of Earth's surface.
Virginia has hills, mountains,
valleys, and a coastal plain.
A landform is the shape of Earth's surface.

Student Edition Do You Know?

1. Name two kinds of landforms in Virginia.

   _____

   -

   _____

2. How might a house near the beach be different from a house in the mountains?

   _____

   -

   _____

   _____

   -

   _____

3. Where is Virginia located in the United States?

   _____

   -

   _____

4. What do you call the kinds of weather an area has over a long period of time?

_____

- -

_____

5. Describe Virginia's climate.

_____

- -

_____

_____

- -

_____

6. What are the four seasons in Virginia?

_____

- -

_____

7. What kind of physical surroundings might make travel very hard?

_____

- -

_____

CHAPTER 7 STUDY GUIDE

Climate

The kinds of weather an area has over a long period of time

Location

The place where a particular point or object exists on the surface of Earth

Physical Surrounding

Land and bodies of water in a given location

Season

Any one of the four phases of the year (winter, spring, summer, or fall)

Landform

A shape or feature of Earth's surface

---

1. The location, climate, and physical surroundings of Virginia affect the way people meet their basic wants. This includes the:

FOODS WE EAT

CLOTHES WE WEAR

HOUSES WE BUILD

2. Communities in Virginia use various types of transportation to meet their needs.

3. The geography of Virginia affects how people travel from one place to another and determines what is available for recreation.

4. The climate of Virginia is mild.

5. Virginia has four distinct seasons that include spring, summer, fall, and winter.

6. Landforms of Virginia include hills, mountains, valleys, and the coastal plain. Landforms affect where people build houses and communities.

7. Virginia is located on the southeastern coast of the United States.

Atlantic Ocean

N
W   E
S

FIRST GRADE
SOL
NEWS

THE ECONOMY

We are all interested in the economy these days.
Involve your child in the decisions that take place in your home.

STANDARDS OF LEARNING

1.7 *The student will explain the difference between goods and services and describe how people are consumers and producers of goods and services.*

1.8 *The student will explain that people make choices because they cannot have everything they want.*

1.9 *The student will recognize that people save money for the future to purchase goods and services.*

Terms to Know

Goods: Things people make or use to satisfy wants

Services: Activities that satisfy people's wants

Consumer: A person who uses goods and services

Producer: A person who makes goods or provides services

Money: Paper bills and coins used to pay for goods and services

Savings: Money not spent now so it can be spent in the future

Cost: What you give up when you decide to do something

Benefit: What satisfies a want

Learning at Home

Children learn by example. Talk with your child about the financial decisions you have to make each day. All families need to buy food and pay for housing expenses. Water and electricity are needs which must come before television services and toys or recreational items. Be sure your child understands that you do not get everything you want. People must choose some things and give up others. Even adults have to make choices and those choices can be very difficult.

You may want to give your child a small allowance each week so that he or she can begin making decisions about spending and saving. Consider using envelopes or savings jars to help your child budget this money. Many authorities suggest using a three-part system. Children can then divide their allowance into three parts: to spend now, to save for later, and to use to help others.

When you visit the grocery store, have your child help you compare prices of similar items and decide which would be the best buy for your money. Give your child the opportunity to pay for small items and to count the change in your pockets.

Use birthdays, holidays, or other occasions to work with your child to produce gifts for friends and relatives. Help your daughter or son understand that the value of a gift does not equal the price paid, but the love and thought involved.

People Provide Services

Name _____

DIRECTIONS: List the services the people provide on the chart below.

Teacher	Chef	Doctor	Firefighter

Sorting Goods and Services

DIRECTIONS: Cut out each box.
Glue them in the correct column of your construction paper.

LET'S GO SHOPPING

Name _____

DIRECTIONS: Pretend you are going grocery shopping.
Draw what goods you would buy at the grocery store in your cart.
Label the goods in your cart.

I Am a Producer and Consumer

Name _____

**DIRECTIONS: Draw and write about how you are
a producer *and* a consumer at school.**

Me as a producer	Me as a consumer
I am a producer when I	**I am a consumer when I**
_____	_____
_____	_____

MY SAVINGS PLAN

Name _____

DIRECTIONS: Fill in the blanks to make a plan for saving money.

I will make a goal to save
$_____.

I will earn this money by
_____
_____.

I will spend this money on
_____
_____.

COSTS AND BENEFITS

Name_____

DIRECTIONS: Cut out the boxes at the bottom. Glue them in the correct places in the chart.

Decision: Should I buy a new toy?		**Decision:** Should I buy a new winter coat?	
Benefit 🙂	**Cost** 🙁	**Benefit** 🙂	**Cost** 🙁

You get to buy one new thing from the store. Should you buy a new toy or a new winter jacket?

- -

I would NOT get to invite my friends over to play with my new toy.	I would get to invite my friends over to play with my new toy.	I would NOT be warm in the cold weather.	I would be very warm during the cold weather.

Economics Word Search

Name_____

DIRECTIONS: Circle the vocabulary words in the word search.

K	K	A	M	N	N	M	R	S	Q	N	F	Y	E	R
N	X	D	C	F	O	E	G	T	K	A	B	B	Q	E
F	E	A	F	N	M	Q	V	S	M	R	O	C	V	C
O	Q	S	E	U	I	B	K	E	C	L	E	R	N	U
W	I	Y	S	M	S	W	T	R	B	P	G	M	J	D
J	D	N	O	L	B	R	D	V	H	I	B	Y	Z	O
E	O	A	X	V	N	E	R	I	D	Y	X	F	M	R
C	Z	R	G	M	G	N	N	C	C	N	P	C	O	P
U	W	H	J	N	J	K	F	E	K	K	H	Y	F	Y
G	W	S	A	V	I	N	G	S	F	S	L	Y	X	T
I	O	O	M	W	N	D	P	U	A	I	F	I	N	F
K	M	O	D	S	P	M	N	S	F	L	T	C	T	U
Z	A	Q	D	N	X	Z	Q	E	V	D	C	G	S	R
T	S	O	C	D	K	M	Q	O	P	L	R	P	K	V
A	G	O	M	C	C	F	H	S	P	S	U	O	A	M

BENEFIT   GOOD   SAVINGS

CONSUMER   MONEY   SERVICE

COST   PRODUCER   SPENDING

Student Edition Do You Know?

1. What is the difference between a good and a service?

   _____

   _____

   _____

   _____

2. What do you use to pay for goods and services?

   _____

   _____

3. What is a consumer?

   _____

   _____

4. What is a producer?

   _____

   _____

5. Why do people save money?

_____

- -

_____

6. Why do people have to make choices?

_____

- -

_____

_____

- -

_____

7. How can a decision-making model help you make a choice?

_____

- -

_____

_____

- -

_____

CHAPTER 8 STUDY GUIDE

GOODS AND SERVICES satisfy people's wants.

Most people are PRODUCERS AND CONSUMERS.

Goods	Things people make or use to satisfy wants
Services	Activities that satisfy people's wants
Consumer	A person who uses or buys goods and services
Producer	A person who makes goods and provides services

All decisions involve COSTS AND BENEFITS.

People cannot have all the goods and services they want. They must choose some things and give up others.

You make better choices when you think about the costs and benefits of your decisions.

Costs	What you give up when you decide to do something
Benefits	What satisfies a want

 People can SPEND OR SAVE money. To save money, people give up spending now in order to buy services or goods in the future.

Money	Paper bills and coins used to pay for goods and services
Savings	Money not spent now so it can be spent in the future

FIRST GRADE SOL NEWS

COMMUNITIES AND GOVERNMENT

"To thrive, even to survive in the 21st century, children will need critical thinking skills, empathetic attitudes, and comfort with a range of human diversity."—Louise Derman-Sparks, Director, Anti-Bias Leadership

STANDARDS OF LEARNING

1.12 b *The student will recognize the symbols and traditional practices that honor the Commonwealth of Virginia by* b) describing why people have symbols and traditions.

1.13 a, b, c *The student will understand that the people of Virginia*
a) have state and local government officials who are elected by voters;
b) make contributions to their communities; and
c) include people who have diverse ethnic origins, customs, and traditions and are united as Americans by common principles.

Terms to Know

tradition: A custom or belief that is practiced or observed over a long period of time. A tradition is a way of doing things that can be passed down from adults to children.

Voters in Virginia elect officials to make decisions for them in the state and local governments.

People contribute to their communities by practicing the responsibilities of good citizenship and volunteering to make communities better.

Many Virginians make valuable contributions to their communities. Communities in Virginia include people of many ethnic origins who come from different places around the world.

People celebrate American holidays and traditions in addition to their own cultural holidays and traditions.

People in Virginia's communities are united as Americans by common principles and traditions, such as
- celebrating Independence Day (Fourth of July)
- pledging allegiance to the flag.

Learning at Home

Our nation has sometimes been called a "Melting Pot," but in truth it is more like a cloak of many colors. Each newcomer to our country weaves a new pattern in the fabric of our communities.

Help your child learn about your family ancestry by working together to create a small scrapbook. Include names and photos of relatives. A small map can be printed and used to show where family members were born.

If possible, ask grandparents and great grandparents to write a short paragraph about where they were born and a fond remembrance. It will be a wonderful legacy for your child.

Talk about family customs and traditions. Do you celebrate any special holidays? How do you celebrate them? What special foods are served in your family? Are there any special clothing items worn on holidays?

Embrace Other Cultures

As you travel with your child throughout your community, look for examples of how other cultures enrich our lives. You can even use a walk through your local grocery store to showcase the contributions of other members of America's family.

146

MY FAMILY CREST

DIRECTIONS: Tell me about your family. Complete each section below with words or pictures.

My family is from...

I have lived in Virginia for _____ years.

My favorite family custom or tradition is...

My favorite American holiday or tradition is...

Members of my family include...

My family name

We Are Off to Volunteer

Sing to the tune of "Here We Go Round the Mulberry Bush."

Off we go to volunteer,
volunteer, volunteer.
Off we go to volunteer,
to make communities better.

Let us show good citizenship,
citizenship, citizenship.
Let us show good citizenship,
to help someone in need.

Helping others is what we do,
what we do, what we do
Helping others is what we do
Because we love our town.

Off we go to volunteer,
volunteer, volunteer.
Off we go to volunteer,
to make communities better.

What Does Our Local Government Do?

DIRECTIONS: Write or draw in the squares to show some of the things our local government does for us.

Parks	Libraries	Public Schools
Police Department	Our Local Government	**Streets**
Public Transportation	**Clean Water**	**Fire Department**

Key Words: Chapter 9

tradition	
diverse	
government	
volunteer	
American principles	

"I VOTE FOR..."

My favorite American principle or tradition is:

☐ **Saying the Pledge of Allegiance**

☐ **Voting**

☐ **Celebrating Independence Day**

TRADITIONS!

Sing to the tune of "My Bonnie Lies Over the Ocean."

Traditions bring people together.
Traditions keep our nation strong.
Traditions bring families together
Each year our traditions go on.

Each year, each year,
From past to the present and beyond.
Each year, each year,
Each year our traditions go on.

Student Edition Do You Know?

1. **Communities in Virginia include people from all over the world. How does this make Virginia a better place?**

   _____

   -

   _____

   _____

   -

   _____

2. **Name two American traditions that bring people in a community together.**

   _____

   -

   _____

   _____

   -

   _____

3. **Who elects the people who run the state and local governments in Virginia?**

   _____

   -

   _____

4. What is a volunteer?

_____

- -

_____

_____

- -

_____

5. Why do communities need volunteers?

_____

- -

_____

_____

- -

_____

CHAPTER 9 STUDY GUIDE

A **TRADITION** is a custom or belief that is practiced or observed over a long period of time.

A tradition is a way of doing things that can be passed down from adults to children.

Communities in Virginia include **DIVERSE** people who come from different places around the world. People celebrate American **HOLIDAYS AND TRADITIONS** in addition to their own cultural holidays and traditions.

People in Virginia's communities are united as Americans by **COMMON PRINCIPLES** and traditions, such as:
• Celebrating Independence Day (Fourth of July)
• Pledging allegiance to the flag

VOTERS in Virginia elect officials to make decisions for them in the state and local **GOVERNMENTS**.

People contribute to their communities by practicing the responsibilities of **GOOD CITIZENSHIP AND VOLUNTEERING** to make communities better. Many Virginians make valuable contributions to their communities.